THE PHONE
DEAD

ANTHONY HOROWITZ

ADAPTED BY TONY LEE • ILLUSTRATED BY DAN BOULTWOOD

First published in 2010
by Franklin Watts

Text © Franklin Watts 2010
Based on the original short story THE PHONE GOES DEAD
Original text © Anthony Horowitz 1999
Illustrations © Dan Boultwood 2010
Cover design by Peter Scoulding

Franklin Watts
338 Euston Road
London NW1 3BH

Franklin Watts Australia
Level 17/207 Kent Street
Sydney, NSW 2000

A CIP catalogue record for this book
is available from the British Library.

ISBN: 978 0 7496 9509 5

1 3 5 7 9 10 8 6 4 2

Printed in China

Franklin Watts is a division of Hachette Children's Books,
an Hachette UK company.
www.hachette.co.uk

This is how Linda James *dies.*

KRA-KOOOM!!

Great. and *today,* of all days!

It has been said that there are *two things* that you shouldn't do in a storm.

The *first* is to make a *telephone call.*

Come *on* - where are you?

Just *great!* Why did I have to pick *today* to forget an umbrella!

Steve - I'm in *Hyde Park* --

The *second* is to take *shelter* under a *tree.*

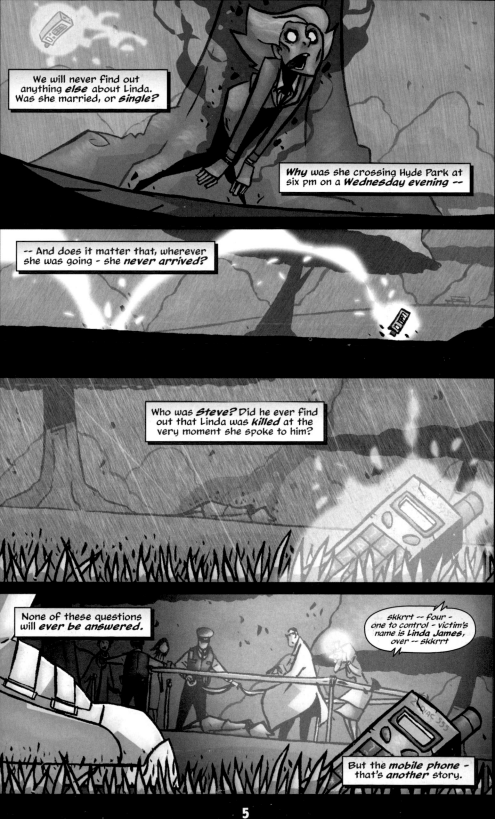

We will never find out anything *else* about Linda. Was she married, or *single?*

Why was she crossing Hyde Park at six pm on a *Wednesday evening* --

-- And does it matter that, wherever she was going - she *never arrived?*

Who was *Steve?* Did he ever find out that Linda was *killed* at the very moment she spoke to him?

None of these questions will *ever be answered.*

skkrrt -- four - one to control - victim's name is *Linda James*, over -- skkrrt

But the *mobile phone* - that's *another* story.

Eric and Mary Saunders used to work for David's father in the hotel - until a year or so back.

1885

Mary left to look after Eric, who'd become sick. *Cancer* or something.

David remembers her - a busy woman with a loud laugh. Always *cheerful* -

Hello? Can I help you?

- At least, until she heard the news about her husband's *illness*.

David! This is a nice surprise! How are you?

She used to bake cakes and would *always* be there with a cup of tea and a slice of something when David got home from school.

I'm fine, thanks, Mrs Saunders.

Do you want to come in?

She was *all right*.

"*I want you to tell her that the ring is under the fridge. She'll understand...*"

No, no thanks - I was just passing on my way home from school.

I was asked to give you a *message*.

17

-- Because he'd *never* taken that ring off - not once in *thirty seven years.*

It was meant to be *buried* with him -

- that was what he'd always *wanted.*

I don't know how you *knew* what you told me - I don't *want* to know how you found out.

But after you left me, I looked under the fridge. The ring was *there* --

-- It must have fallen off his finger and *rolled* there. Anyway, David, I wanted you to know -

- I found the ring and the Vicar's arranged for it to be put in the grave with my Eric.

It means a *lot* to me. I'm *glad* you told me what you did.

I'm glad...

David couldn't work it out. Her face...

...She looked *scared* of him.

25

Newport library,
Isle of Wight.

Hi, do you
have a phone
directory?

Sure. In
the *reference*
section. Over
there.

READ.

FETE

Darwin...
Davenport...
Davidge...
Davies.

Davies,
Marion - Eleven,
St Edwards Square.
So she *does*
exist.

But what
happened to
Samantha?
Did she
die?

Hey -
do you have
file copies of the
local paper for
the last year on
microfilm?

Or maybe
scanned on a
computer?

No.

We have
archive copies
of each paper
though.

Could
I see them?
Maybe the
last *year's*
worth?

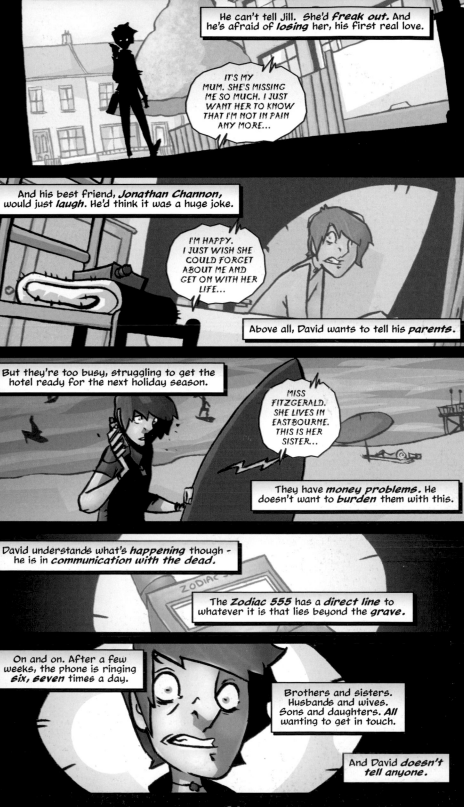

He can't tell Jill. She'd *freak out.* And he's afraid of *losing* her, his first real love.

IT'S MY MUM. SHE'S MISSING ME SO MUCH. I JUST WANT HER TO KNOW THAT I'M NOT IN PAIN ANY MORE...

And his best friend, *Jonathan Channon,* would just *laugh.* He'd think it was a huge joke.

I'M HAPPY. I JUST WISH SHE COULD FORGET ABOUT ME AND GET ON WITH HER LIFE...

Above all, David wants to tell his *parents.*

But they're too busy, struggling to get the hotel ready for the next holiday season.

MISS FITZGERALD. SHE LIVES IN EASTBOURNE. THIS IS HER SISTER...

They have *money problems.* He doesn't want to *burden* them with this.

David understands what's *happening* though - he is in *communication with the dead.*

The *Zodiac 555* has a *direct line* to whatever it is that lies beyond the *grave.*

ZODIAC

On and on. After a few weeks, the phone is ringing *six, seven* times a day.

Brothers and sisters. Husbands and wives. Sons and daughters. *All* wanting to get in touch.

And David *doesn't tell anyone.*

35

Well, I see everyone anyway.

I'm sorry, I don't much like using it.

Well it's a bit of a *waste of money*.

I'm paying the *line rental*, after all.

Where is the phone? You haven't *lost it* have you?

You know, you could *tell us* if you had.

It's in my bedroom.

Well if you don't want it, your father might as well cancel the *contract*. Just give it back.

Really?

Yeah! Sure! Whatever you say!

This food is *awesome*, Mum!

Kids!

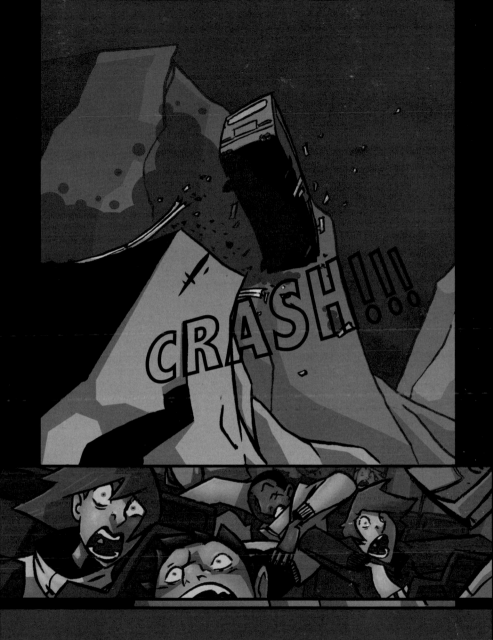

ANTHONY HOROWITZ

Anthony's mum used to read him horror stories when he was eight years old, and this is the inevitable result. He has been called the busiest writer in England and is best known for his ALEX RIDER novels which have sold over twelve million copies worldwide. He used to write in a garden shed until his wife sold the garden. Now he lives and works in London.

TONY LEE

Tony has been writing for over twenty years, and has worked on X-MEN, SPIDER MAN and recently DOCTOR WHO for IDW. His graphic novel OUTLAW: THE LEGEND OF ROBIN HOOD for Walker Books was on the ALA 'Best of 2010' list. Tony is also adapting Anthony Horowitz's POWER OF FIVE series for Walker Books.

DAN BOULTWOOD

Dan has illustrated several critically acclaimed graphic novels, including THE GLOOM and HOPE FALLS for Markosia, THE PRINCE OF BAGHDAD for Random House and G.P. Taylor's THE DOPPLEGANGER CHRONICLES for Tyndale Press.

THE PHONE GOES DEAD by Anthony Horowitz was originally published by Orchard Books. Check out all the frightfully good HOROWITZ HORROR titles at: www.orchardbooks.co.uk

Don't pick up...

ANTHONY
HOROWITZ
THE PHONE GOES DEAD

EVER DIALLED A WRONG NUMBER..?

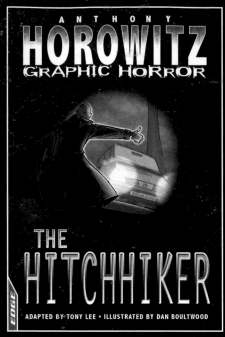
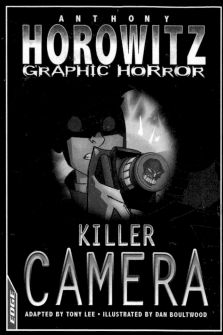
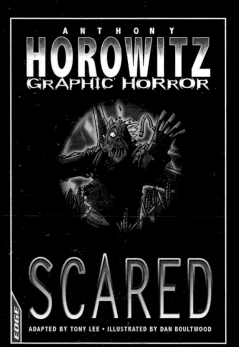